ANGELMOUSE

Lost Thingamajig

by Rodney Peppé

It was a beautiful morning, but Angelmouse was in a very bad mood. The whole house shook as he hurtled round it. He was looking for something.

"Angelmouse! What is the matter?" called Quilly.
"My thingamajig!" yelled Angelmouse. "It's gone!"

"Help me find it!" screamed Angelmouse.

"Please," said Quilly.

"Oh," said a scowling Angelmouse, "**Please**…"

They searched the house for the missing halo.

"It must be outside somewhere," said Angelmouse.

Quilly and Angelmouse flew in and out of the clouds. They searched all over the place, but it wasn't anywhere to be seen.
Then Angelmouse
spotted something...

"There!" he cried. "There it is!"

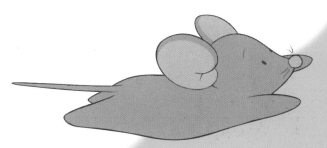

Elliemum and Baby Ellie were playing with a hoop in their garden. Suddenly, Angelmouse swooped down from the sky. "Give it back!" he shouted. "That's my thingamajig!"

"No it's not!" protested Elliemum. "It's Baby Ellie's hoop."

"Now look what you've done," said Elliemum.
"You've frightened her away!"
"Say sorry, Angelmouse!" demanded Quilly.
But Angelmouse wouldn't say sorry.
"We'll help you find Baby Ellie."
Quilly promised Elliemum.
"Not until I find my
thingamajig,"
shouted Angelmouse rudely.

Later on, Angelmouse spotted Hutchkin
having breakfast outside his burrow.

"Mmmm! Nice!" he said as he opened his
mouth to munch a large doughnut.

Suddenly…

WHOOSH! Angelmouse dive-bombed him
and grabbed the doughnut!

"Hey man…!" began Hutchkin.

"You can't eat my
thingamajig!"
screamed Angelmouse.

Angelmouse put the doughnut above his head. It dropped down and became a sticky mess.

"That's my doughnut, man," said Hutchkin.

Just then Quilly arrived. "Sorry, we'll get you another one, Hutchkin," he promised.

"**You** can," said Angelmouse, scattering crumbs behind him as he took off. "I've got to find my thingamajig."

Angelmouse swooped down on Spencer. "Where's my thingamajig?" he demanded.

"What's a thingamajig? Is it a hat?" asked Spencer.

"No! Not a hat," snapped Angelmouse. "I mean the round shiny thing that angels have. I've lost it."

Just then Oswald the duck came speeding towards them.
"No brakes! No brakes!" he cried. "Help! Help!"
"Oh, I say, look out!" cried Spencer.

"What's the matter, Oswald?" he asked.

"Baby Ellie! Baby Ellie!" gabbled Oswald. "Pond! Pond!"

"How did that happen?" asked Spencer.

Angelmouse remembered how he'd frightened Baby Ellie.

"It might have been my fault," he said sadly.

"Follow me!" cried Oswald. "Follow me!"
All the friends followed Oswald. Everyone was
going to help Baby Ellie.

Poor Baby Ellie was in the middle of the pond, sinking into the muddy water. How could they reach her?

"My poor baby!" wailed Elliemum. "Please help her."

"Look," Angelmouse cried, pointing to a life-belt.
"Forget about your thingamajig," said Quilly.
"We've got to rescue Baby Ellie."

"That's what I'm doing," said Angelmouse. **"Help me!"**
Angelmouse took the rope, and, with Quilly's help,
flew over to Baby Ellie and dropped the life-belt.

"Catch, Baby Ellie, catch!"
shouted Angelmouse.

Baby Ellie was safer now, with the life-belt around her.

"I need you all to help," said Angelmouse.

Everyone lined up on the bank.

"One…" said Spencer.

"Two…" said Quilly.

"Three. Three…" said Oswald.

"**PULL**," shouted Angelmouse.

"WHEEEE!" Baby Ellie cried happily, as she came sliding out of the pond.

"You're an angel, Angelmouse!" declared Elliemum. "You saved my Baby Ellie!" She gave the mouse a big noisy kiss.

Just then Spencer noticed something…
"Angelmouse, look," he said. "There's your thinga…"
Angelmouse reached above his head.
"My thingamajig!" he cried. "It's back!"

Angelmouse admired the reflection of his halo in the pond. "As soon as you did something good," said Quilly, "It came back straight away."

"And it's extra bright," said Angelmouse.
"Well," said Quilly, "you've been **extra** good!"